# Ranches
# and Rainbows

PINE STREET SCHOOL

### • ODILLE OUSLEY

**GINN AND COMPANY** | BOSTON · NEW YORK · CHICAGO · ATLANTA
DALLAS · PALO ALTO · TORONTO · LONDON

# Acknowledgments

Artists and Writers Guild, Inc., for our adaptation of "Ellie, the Elephant" (Ellie Phantastic), by Doris M. Fletcher, from *The Golden Grab Bag of Stories, Poems, and Songs*, edited by Jerome Wyckoff, copyright 1951, by Simon and Schuster, Inc., and Artists and Writers Guild, Inc.

Alfred Boyd and *Jack and Jill* for our adaptation of "Ride and Tie," copyright 1948, by The Curtis Publishing Company.

Eleanor A. Chaffee and *American Junior Red Cross News* for the poem "The Cobbler," copyright 1938, by The American National Red Cross.

Childrens Press, Inc., for "Excitement on Applegate Street," adapted from *Excitement in Appleby Street* by Eda and Richard Crist, copyright 1950, by Childrens Press, Inc.

Lillian Doherty and *Jack and Jill* for "Jingle, the Monkey," adapted from "Sammy, Susie, and Peter Have an Exciting Day," copyright 1947, by The Curtis Publishing Company. Reprinted by special permission from *Jack and Jill*.

Berta Donahue and *Story Parade* for "The Talking Horse," adapted from "The Horse That Talked," copyright 1952, by *Story Parade*.

Nona Keen Duffy and *Child Life* for the poem "Cowboy Song," copyright 1953, by *Child Life*.

E. P. Dutton & Company, Inc., for our adaptation of "Fleetfoot's First Shoes," from *Farmtown Tales* by Mary W. Thompson. Copyright 1923, by E. P. Dutton & Company, Inc.; renewal 1951, by Mary W. Thompson.

Margaret A. Hamilton for "Aunt Daisy and Her Things," adapted from "Dame Huggins Makes a Discovery" in *Highlights for Children*, March, 1949, by permission of *Highlights for Children*.

Harcourt, Brace and Company, Inc., for the poem "Buildings" from *Whispers and Other Poems*, copyright 1958, by Myra Cohn Livingston. Reprinted by permission of Harcourt, Brace and Company, Inc.

2

# Stories in This Book

## On the Ranch

## Just for Fun

## Around Rainbow Corners

4

# Horses and Horses

# Along City Streets

# Old, Old Stories

# On the Ranch

# Randy and the Red Rocket

Randy stopped near the ranch house and listened. He could hear a train coming. The train was still far down the track.

Randy liked to ride across the field to watch the long train go by.

" Get up, Ginger! " said Randy. " The train is coming. If we hurry, we will be in time to see it."

Away Randy and Ginger went.

8

The big engine pulled the long train down the track.

Then, bump! Bump! B-u-m-p! The old black engine stopped. All the cars in the long train stopped too.

There were cars loaded with cows and cars loaded with corn. There were many other cars too.

Randy saw Mr. Joe at the window of the big engine.

"What is the matter, Mr. Joe?" called Randy. "Why have you stopped on the side track today?"

"We are waiting here for something," called Mr. Joe.

Randy jumped off Ginger and climbed up on the fence.

"What are you waiting for, Mr. Joe?" called Randy.

"We are waiting here so the Red Rocket can go by," said Mr. Joe.

"The Red Rocket!" said Randy. "And what is that, Mr. Joe?"

"The Red Rocket is a very fast new train," said Mr. Joe. "We pulled over here to this side track so the fast train can go right through."

Just then Randy heard a low roar. The Red Rocket was coming down the track. It was coming fast!

"Here it comes," called Mr. Joe. "What an engine! What a train!"

Swish-sh-sh! Swish-sh-sh! went the Red Rocket.

"Boy!" said Randy. "What a train!"

Then the Red Rocket was gone. And so was Ginger!

Ginger did not like the roar of the Red Rocket. He ran away from the train as fast as he could go.

Randy called to Ginger, but he did not come back. Up went his head and across the field he ran.

Randy jumped down from the fence. He waved to Mr. Joe as the long train pulled off the side track.

Then Randy started for home, but he did not get there very soon. He had to walk all the way.

12

## Ginger Plays Tag

"Ginger came home, Randy," called Jill. "I opened the gate and he went into the corral."

Randy went to the fence and called to Ginger, but Ginger did not come.

"Our Ginger is frisky today," said Randy. "He thinks that he is still running away from the Red Rocket."

Jill said, "We must catch Ginger now, Randy. Mother wants you to go to the store for her."

Then Jill saw Father coming across the yard to the corral.

"Father, please come and help us catch Ginger," called Jill.

Father had a feed box in his hand. He walked over to the corral fence.

"I have some feed in this box," said Father. "Let's see if you can make the feed-box trick work."

Randy took the feed box. Then he opened the big corral gate and started toward Ginger. Randy did not walk very fast.

14

Ginger saw the feed box, so he started to walk toward Randy.

Randy walked on with the feed box. But Ginger stopped. Then he turned and ran away as fast as he could.

" Stay where you are now, Randy," called Father. " Ginger will soon come to the feed box, but he wants to play tag with you first."

Ginger did play tag. First he ran this way. Then he ran that way. But at last he started toward Randy and the feed box.

The children watched and waited.

15

On came Ginger. At first he ran. Then he walked. He came right up and put his nose into the feed box.

"I have you now," said Randy. And he jumped on Ginger's back.

Jill sat on the corral fence. She waved to Randy as he rode away.

"Ginger likes to play tag," she said. "But Randy can play tag, too!"

When Randy got to the store, he tied Ginger to a post nearby.

Ginger was right there waiting when Randy came out of the store.

"No more tag today!" said Randy as he jumped on Ginger and rode away.

Used by permission of the publisher, J. B. Lippincott Company, from *Cloverfield Farm Stories*, by Helen Fuller Orton. Copyright 1921, 1922, 1924, 1926, by Helen Fuller Orton.

# Ride and Tie

One morning Randy and his horse Ginger stopped in front of Jack's house.

"Are you ready now, Jack?" called Randy. "It's about time for us to start for the rodeo."

Jack ran out of the ranch house when he heard Randy call.

"I cannot go after all, Randy," said Jack. "Father needs to use my horse this morning."

17

Randy and Jack looked at each other. They had been counting on going to the rodeo for a long time.

" What shall we do ? " asked Randy.

The two boys sat on the corral fence and thought and thought.

" There must be a way for us to get to the rodeo," said Randy.

" It is too far to walk," said Jack. " We would not get to the rodeo in time if we walked."

" I wish we could ride on Ginger," said Randy. " But Ginger is funny. He will buck like a bronco if two boys get on his back at the same time."

The boys went on thinking. Then Jack said, " I know how we can get there. We can ride and tie."

" Ride and tie ! " said Randy. " What kind of game is that ? "

18

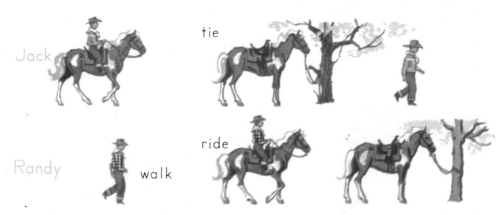

Jack     tie

Randy    walk    ride

"That's the way two boys used to go on a trip with just one horse," said Jack. "I read about it once in a book."

"How did it work?" asked Randy.

"Like this," said Jack. "Two boys would start from the same place. One boy would ride. The other boy would walk down the same road."

Randy listened as Jack went on.

"After a while the boy on horseback would get off. Then he would tie the horse to a tree and start walking. The horse would wait there for the other boy to come along and ride."

19

"Let's go, Jack!" said Randy. "You ride first and I'll start walking. When you get to the ranch store, tie Ginger. Then I can ride him from the store to the rodeo."

Jack ran to tell his father what he and Randy were going to do.

Soon the two boys were on their way. Jack rode away on Ginger, and Randy started to walk along the road toward the rodeo.

The boys got to the rodeo at about the same time. When Randy rode up on Ginger, Jack was there waiting.

20

"Come on!" called Randy. "We are just in time to see the bucking broncos."

Soon the two boys were watching the rodeo. They saw the cowboys ride the bucking broncos. They watched the rope tricks and the pony races too.

When the rodeo was over, there was Jack's father waiting by the gate. So the boys did not have to ride and tie on the way home.

# Cowboy Song

Come mount your pony
  And I shall mount mine.
We'll go to the round-up,
  Come rain or shine.

With packs on each saddle,
  We'll gallop away
Singing, " Yip-pee-ki !
  Yip-pee-ki !  Yi-pee-ki-yay ! "

We'll cook by a campfire,
  And spread out our bed.
We'll sleep on the ground
  With the sky for a spread.

We'll whirl our long ropes
  And here's what we'll say,
" Yip-pee-ki !  Yip-pee-ki !
  Yip-pee-ki-yay ! "

*Nona Keen Duffy*

22

# The Twin Calves

"Jill! Come here, Jill," shouted Randy. "Come and see the twin calves that Father just brought home."

"Twin calves!" said Jill. And out of the house she ran.

Randy and Jill thought the little twin calves were beautiful.

"The twin calves are yours," said Father. "The mother cow will stay here in the yard. You can help take care of her and the twins."

"That will be fun," said Jill.

Each day the children brought food to the mother cow. Then they brought water for the twin calves. They had fun playing with the calves, too.

One day Randy said, " Father, may we tie ropes on the twin calves ? We want to take them to the house."

" Please, Father," said Jill. " We want to show them to Mother. May we ? "

Father laughed. " Yes," he said. " I will help you tie ropes on the calves. But see that you don't let them get into your mother's flower garden. She would not like that ! "

Father helped Randy and Jill tie a rope to each of the calves.

Then Father opened the gate for the twin calves. They were gone with the children before the mother cow knew what was happening.

24

Just then the mother cow saw that her calves were outside the fence. She didn't like that at all!

The mother cow ran to the gate. Then up went her head.

" Moo-o ! " she called. " Moo-o-o ! "

The twin calves heard their mother call. They stopped! They listened!

" Moo-o-o-o ! " she called again.

Then the calves started back to the gate, and they ran right through Mother's flower garden on the way. Randy and Jill ran after them.

25

" Oh, Randy ! " said Jill. " Just look at
Mother's flowers ! What shall we do ? "

" We must find Mother," said Randy.
" We must tell her about this. We
must tell her right away."

In the back door of the ranch house
the children ran. They were in such
a hurry that they left the door open
behind them.

Mother was not in the kitchen. So the
children ran to the front of the house
looking for her.

The twin calves tried to get back to their mother. But they soon found that she was on the other side of the fence, so they could not reach her.

Then the calves started to walk all around the yard outside the fence. They walked on through the back yard until they came to the ranch house.

Soon the calves saw that the back door of the house was open. They went to the door and looked in. Then the two little calves walked right into the big ranch kitchen.

The two calves looked all around the big ranch kitchen. Then they started across the kitchen floor. Bump, bump, bump! they went.

The calves saw the pan of milk for the cats. It was near the door. They put their noses down into the milk. It was good! Soon the milk was gone.

Then the calves started to walk around again. Bump, bump, bump!

The children's mother heard the noise in the kitchen.

"Listen!" she said. "What's that?"

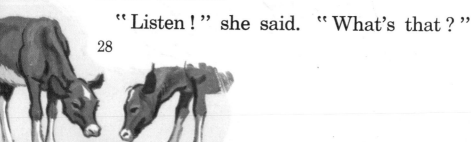

Mother went out to the kitchen in a hurry, but she stopped at the door.

"It's the two calves!" called Mother. "Randy! Jill! Come and get them out of the kitchen right now!"

The children came running.

"Get out, you two! Get out!" said Randy. "Go back to the yard!"

Just then the mother cow called to her twins again. And away the calves ran like little bucking broncos.

The children's mother watched the calves go. Then she laughed.

29

"They must be good calves," said Mother. "They go to their mother when they hear her call."

Randy ran after the calves. This time he opened the gate and they ran right into the yard.

The twin calves were happy to be with their mother again.

The next day Randy and Jill did not play with the calves. They worked in Mother's flower garden.

Randy and Jill did not take the twin calves into the back yard again. Not for a long, long time!

# Just
# for Fun

31

## Mrs. Turtle and the New Hat

Mrs. Duck looked at the big new sign in the window of her hat store.

"I shall sell many of my new hats today," she said. "They are all such beautiful hats!"

Mrs. Duck went to open the door for Mrs. Goose.

Mrs. Goose tried on a red hat. It had a long, long feather on it.

"Very pretty!" said Mrs. Goose.

Just then Mrs. Turtle stopped by the open door and looked in.

"Oh, do come in, Mrs. Turtle!" said Mrs. Duck. "Come in and let me find a pretty hat for you."

Mrs. Turtle crawled into the hat store and looked all around.

"Yes, I think I would like a hat," said Mrs. Turtle. "A little pink hat!"

Mrs. Duck put a pretty little hat on Mrs. Turtle's head. It was a pink hat with a blue feather on it.

"This hat looks wonderful on you, Mrs. Turtle," said Mrs. Duck. "It was just made for you!"

Mrs. Turtle looked at the front of the pink hat. Then she took a small looking glass and looked at the back of the hat.

"I think it looks wonderful!" said Mrs. Turtle. "Just wonderful! I have never had a hat before, but I will take this one, please."

So Mrs. Turtle went out of the hat store with a new pink hat. The new hat was on her head and her head was high in the air!

Down the street Mrs. Turtle went, trick-track, trick-track, trick-track.

34

Soon Mrs. Turtle met a big dog.

Now Mrs. Turtle was afraid of dogs.
So she pulled her head into her shell.
And swish! Off went the new pink hat!

Soon the dog went on his way. Then
Mrs. Turtle put her head out of her shell
and looked all around for her new hat.
It was on the grass not far away.

"Oh me! Oh my!" said Mrs. Turtle
as she looked at her hat. "My shell
is my house. I cannot get a hat into
my house. I never thought of that!"

35

Mrs. Turtle picked up her new hat and took it back to Mrs. Duck's store.

"I have just found out something," Mrs. Turtle said to Mrs. Duck.

"What?" asked Mrs. Duck. "What have you found out, Mrs. Turtle?"

"Hats may be all right for rabbits and squirrels and ducks," said Mrs. Turtle. "But now I know that hats are not made for turtles."

"Why not?" said Mrs. Duck. "This is a beautiful hat. Let me put it on your head again, Mrs. Turtle."

"Now watch and I will show you something," said Mrs. Turtle.

Into her shell went Mrs. Turtle's head. And off went the new pink hat!

Mrs. Duck laughed. "I see!" she said. "I have learned something I never knew before. Now I know why hats are not for turtles."

Mrs. Duck put the hat back on her hat table. And Mrs. Turtle crawled off to her own little pond.

"Hats are just not for turtles," she said. Then she pulled her head inside her shell and went to sleep.

37

# Turtle

I have not heard a turtle talk,
Or even make a sound;
But I have watched a turtle walk—
    Trick-track,
    Trick-track—
Slowly on the ground.

I have not felt a turtle bite,
Or seen it snap its jaws;
But I have followed trick-track trails
Of a turtle's claws.

And I have seen a turtle pull
Its head and legs, and tail as well,
Quickly into safety
Inside its hard clean shell.

*James S. Tippett*

## At the Animal Show

Father Monkey sat in his big chair looking at the Animal Town newspaper.

Little Monkey was looking at the newspaper, too. He saw a picture of a big circus that was coming to town.

"I would like to go
To the animal show!"

said Little Monkey.

"So would I!" said Father Monkey. "I will get the tickets on my way home tonight. Then we can all go."

Little Monkey began to dance around and around. He sang,

"We are going to go
To the animal show!"

"Do you suppose Green Turtle and Gray Elephant would like to go too?" asked Father Monkey.

"I know they would. Animal shows are fun!" said Little Monkey.

"Then you may ask them to go with us," said Father Monkey.

Away ran Little Monkey. He wanted to tell Green Turtle and Gray Elephant the good news right away.

40

The next day they all got ready to go to the animal show. Father Monkey put on his new blue suit and a bright yellow tie. Mother Monkey put on her pretty blue dress and her new red hat.

Little Monkey and Gray Elephant and Green Turtle dressed in their best, too. How fine they all looked as they walked along together!

It was a beautiful day. The sun was bright and the sky was blue.

Little Monkey danced along the road and sang,

"We are on our way
To the show today!"

It was not long before the others were singing with Little Monkey.

"I can see the big circus tents now," called Father Monkey. "Hurry!"

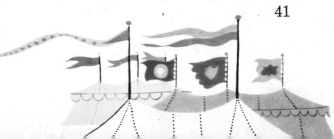

Father Monkey walked right up to the gate. Mr. Lion was there ready to take the tickets.

Father Monkey took the tickets out of his pocket and handed them to Mr. Lion.

Mr. Lion counted the five tickets. Then he looked at Father and Mother Monkey. He looked at Little Monkey and Green Turtle. Then he looked at Gray Elephant!

"You do not have enough tickets," said Mr. Lion. "Gray Elephant needs five seats all by himself!"

42

Father Monkey turned and looked at Gray Elephant. He saw how very big Gray Elephant was.

"No, we do not have enough seats," said Father Monkey. And he put the tickets back into his pocket.

Then they all turned around and started to go back home.

Just then Little Monkey thought of something. He called out,

"I know! I know!
How we can go!"

Then he went to Gray Elephant and whispered something in his ear.

43

Gray Elephant looked pleased. He whispered something to Father Monkey.

Father Monkey whispered something to Mr. Lion and gave the five tickets back to him again. Then they all walked inside the big circus tent to their seats.

Gray Elephant did take up all five seats, but they did not need any more.

Gray Elephant was so big that he could hold all the others. So they saw the animal show after all.

44

## Aunt Daisy and Her Things

Once there was a little old woman named Aunt Daisy.

Aunt Daisy lived in a little white house. She had all kinds of things in her house. Pets! Dishes! Clothes!

Aunt Daisy had one trouble. She could never find anything when she needed it. She was always looking for something that was lost.

One day Aunt Daisy said, " I spend too much time looking for things. I will go and ask my friend Mrs. King what I can do about my trouble."

45

Aunt Daisy climbed out of bed early the next morning. She wanted to get an early start for her trip to Mrs. King's house.

She began to have trouble right away. She could not find her shoes.

Aunt Daisy looked all over the house. At last she found her shoes under the kitchen table.

Soon she had more trouble. She just couldn't find the pan for her breakfast pancakes. And Aunt Daisy did like pancakes! She made such good ones!

At last Aunt Daisy found the pan, so now she could make some pancakes for her breakfast.

After she ate all the pancakes, she did not have enough time to go and see her friend Mrs. King.

" I'll wait and go tomorrow," she said. " That's what I will do ! "

Before Aunt Daisy went to bed that night she put the pan for her pancakes on the stove. Then she put her shoes under her bed.

" There ! " she said. " Tomorrow I shall know right where my things are. So I can get an early start."

47

The next morning Aunt Daisy was up very early.

"I must hurry and get dressed," she said. She found her shoes under the bed right where she had put them.

In a short time, Aunt Daisy was ready for breakfast. She found her pan at once and made some pancakes. Then she ate her breakfast.

"I shall be ready very soon," said Aunt Daisy. "But before I go, I must find the cat's dish. I want to give her some milk."

48

Aunt Daisy looked and looked for the cat's dish. At last she found it.

By now it was dinner time. So she did not go to Mrs. King's after all.

"I'll go tomorrow," said Aunt Daisy. "Mrs. King will know just what to do about my trouble."

Before Aunt Daisy went to bed that night she put her shoes under the bed. She put her pan on the stove. Then she got the cat's dish and put it on the floor by the stove.

"Tomorrow I will get an early start," thought Aunt Daisy. Then she went to sleep.

The next morning Aunt Daisy found her things in a hurry. Soon she was ready to go to Mrs. King's.

"Oh my!" said Aunt Daisy as she opened her front door. "It is much too early now to go to see Mrs. King. How did I ever get ready so soon?"

Aunt Daisy sat down in her rocking chair to think the matter over.

She rocked and she thought, and she thought and she rocked. All at once she stopped rocking.

Then Aunt Daisy said, "I know why I got ready so early today. I didn't have to look for a thing. Not one thing! How wonderful!"

Aunt Daisy began to laugh.

"I shall not have to go to Mrs. King with my trouble after all," she said. "All I have to do to find things is to put them where they belong."

Aunt Daisy stayed at home all day. She put all her things right where they belonged.

"How wonderful!" said Aunt Daisy as she looked around her little house that night.

"I shall never have trouble finding my things again," she said. "I will keep everything in its place. That is what I will do!"

And she did!

# The Horse in the House

It was moving day for the Mulligans. But they were not moving very far.

Their new house was right next to their old gray farmhouse.

All day the Mulligans were busy with their moving. When night came, the bed in the new house was made and a fire was burning in the stove.

Mrs. Mulligan stirred the soup on the stove. Then she looked out of the window at the old house.

"The old house looks so empty!" said Mrs. Mulligan. "What are we to do with the old place, Pat?"

"We could use it for a barn," said Pat Mulligan.

"And why not?" said Mrs. Mulligan. "We have been wanting a pig and a cow and some hens. Now we have a place to put them!"

"That we have!" said Mr. Mulligan. "We have a barn. So now we can have some animals of our own."

"How I wish Aunt Bridget could see us!" said Mrs. Mulligan. "She would be surprised to see how we have come up in the world."

53

The old gray house made a fine barn for the animals.

First, Pat Mulligan bought an old horse from his friend Mike.

"Let's put the horse in the front room," said Mrs. Mulligan. "She will like the pretty green walls."

Then the Mulligans put a cow in the kitchen. They got some pigs for the little back room too. And hens were everywhere.

"Oh, I tell you this old gray house is just the place for all our animals," said Mr. Mulligan.

One morning when Mrs. Mulligan was out feeding the hens, she heard Pat calling to her.

"Here is a letter for you," he said. "It just came. I think it is from your Aunt Bridget."

Mrs. Mulligan was in a great hurry to find out what the letter said.

"Will you listen to this, Pat!" said Mrs. Mulligan. "Aunt Bridget will stop by next Saturday to see us."

"That's very good news," said Mr. Mulligan. "And to think that your Aunt Bridget doesn't know a thing about the new house. We will surprise her!"

"Oh my, yes," said Mrs. Mulligan. "What a surprise she will get!"

The next day Mrs. Mulligan cleaned the new house. Then she made cakes. All kinds of cakes!

Mrs. Mulligan was so busy that she did not hear Aunt Bridget's carriage come into the yard next door.

Aunt Bridget was all dressed up in a purple hat and a long purple dress.

She got out of her shiny black carriage and started up the walk toward the old gray house.

Aunt Bridget went right up to the front door and looked for the bell. But there was no bell, so she opened the door and walked right in!

56

Aunt Bridget came out of the house in a hurry! "Help! Help!" she called. "There is a horse in the house!"

The old horse was standing in the open door looking very much surprised.

The cow looked out of the kitchen window to see what was happening. And the hens made all kinds of noises. Loud hen noises!

Aunt Bridget ran down the walk in a hurry. She waved her hands in the air and called, "Help! Help!"

Mrs. Mulligan was busy in her new house, but she heard all the noise at the house next door.

She went to the kitchen window and looked out. What a surprise she had!

"She's here!" called Mrs. Mulligan. "Aunt Bridget is here, Pat. She's over at the little gray house now!"

Mr. and Mrs. Mulligan ran toward the old gray house.

"There's a horse in the house!" called Aunt Bridget. "And a cow! Who ever heard of bringing farm animals into the house!"

"Oh, Aunt Bridget, we do not live in the old gray house now," said Mrs. Mulligan. "We have a new house right next door."

"And we have animals now too," said Mr. Mulligan. "The animals live in this old house."

Aunt Bridget laughed and laughed, and so did the Mulligans.

The horse was still at the open door watching them. She did not know what they were laughing at, for she was just a horse. A horse that liked to live in a house!

## Fisherman Fred

It was a fine morning in spring and Fisherman Fred was going to sea. He walked down the street singing,

> "Hi, hi, ho! Hi, hi, hee!
> I'm going to catch a fish
> When I go out to sea."

The butcher heard Fred singing and called, "Catch one for me!"

Fisherman Fred laughed and said, "I'll do just that." And he danced a hornpipe right in the street.

The baker heard Fisherman Fred and ran to the door.

"Catch one for me!" he cried.

"I'll be glad to do just that," said Fisherman Fred. And again he sang,

> "Hi, hi, ho! Hi, hi, hee!
> I'm going to catch a fish
> When I go out to sea."

The grocer heard Fisherman Fred and called, "Catch one for me!"

Fisherman Fred laughed and said, "I'll do just that." And again he danced on his way to the sea.

61

Fisherman Fred soon came to the shore where his boat was tied. Down over the rocks and into the boat he climbed.

Soon he was rowing and singing,

> "Hi, hi, ho! Hi, hi, hee!
> The butcher and the baker
> And the grocer make three.
> I'm going to catch some fish
> While I am on the sea!"

Fisherman Fred reached a quiet place and let his line down into the sea.

Very soon Fisherman Fred had a fish
on his line.

" That's for the butcher," he said.
Then he put his line back into the sea.

Fisherman Fred pulled one fish and
then another out of the sea.

" Here's a fish for the baker and one
for the grocer," said he.

Fisherman Fred pulled in his line and
started his boat toward home.

When he reached the shore, he tied his
boat. Then over the rocks he climbed
to the street.

Fisherman Fred went on singing,

"Hi, hi, ho! Hi, hi, hee!
I got three fish
When I went to sea.
The butcher and the baker
And the grocer make three.
But I never did think
To catch a fish for me!"

The butcher heard Fred singing and ran to the door.

"Have dinner with me tonight," called the butcher.

Fisherman Fred laughed and said, "I'll do just that!"

The baker heard Fisherman Fred and called to him, "Have dinner with me tomorrow night."

"I'll be glad to do just that," said Fisherman Fred.

"Come and have dinner with me the next night," called the grocer.

Fisherman Fred laughed and said, "I'll do just that."

Fisherman Fred gave the three fish to his friends. Then he went to his own house singing all the way,

"Hi, hi, ho! Hi, hi, hee!
I'm happy as happy can be."

65

Fisherman Fred put on his good coat and his best shoes. Then back to the butcher's house he went.

"I didn't think to catch a fish for myself," said Fisherman Fred. "But there are three dinners for me."

And he laughed as he walked along.

"One dinner with the butcher! One with the baker! One with the grocer! A lucky fisherman am I," he said.

Down the street he went singing,

"Hi, hi, ho! Hi, hi, hee!
I'm happy as happy can be.
For dinners have I —
One, two, three."

# Around Rainbow Corners

## The Squeak Box

Mother picked up one of Bonnie's red shoes and looked at it.

"Just look at this shoe, Bonnie!" said Mother. "It needs to go to Mr. Bob's shop today."

"I'm going to town right now," said Father. "I can drop Bonnie and Billy at Mr. Bob's shop."

The children ran out and got into Father's old truck. Very soon they were bumping along the road on their way to Rainbow Corners.

Bonnie and Billy always liked to go to Mr. Bob's shop. They liked to watch Mr. Bob as he worked on their shoes. But best of all, the children liked to hear Mr. Bob talk.

Mr. Bob was very glad to see the children. He started to work on Bonnie's shoe at once. He talked to the children as he worked.

" Did I ever tell you about my old squeak box ? " asked Mr. Bob.

" No ! " said Billy. " Tell us about your squeak box, Mr. Bob."

" Please, Mr. Bob ! " said Bonnie.

69

The children sat down on a long seat near the old stove to listen. They always listened when Mr. Bob talked.

"Well," said Mr. Bob. "Once there was a little girl who had some new shoes that squeaked."

Mr. Bob worked a little more and then went on with his story.

"This little girl's new shoes squeaked when she walked. They squeaked when she ran. They went squeak, squeak, squeak, all over town."

"Who was this little girl, Mr. Bob?" asked Billy.

"I cannot tell you who she was," said Mr. Bob. "But one day she came to me with her shoes and what do you think I did?"

"What?" asked Bonnie. "What did you do, Mr. Bob?"

"I took the squeak out," said Mr. Bob. "See that long black box?"

Bonnie and Billy looked up at the long black box.

"Yes," said Mr. Bob. "I put the squeak in that box with all my other squeaks. I guess it's there still!"

71

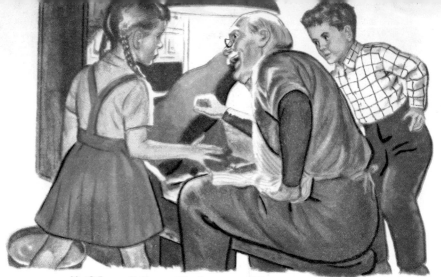

"Oh, Mr. Bob, will you open your squeak box, please," said Bonnie. "I want to see all the squeaks."

Mr. Bob laughed. He took down the squeak box. Then he sat down on the seat with the box beside him.

"Well now," said Mr. Bob. "What if a squeak jumps out when I open the box! It might jump right into your shoe! Then you would be in trouble!"

The children laughed.

"Please, Mr. Bob," they said. "Please open the box now! Hurry!"

Mr. Bob opened the squeak box and the children looked inside.

Then they began to laugh. The children laughed and laughed. Mr. Bob laughed with them.

"It's a fiddle," cried Billy. "Your big squeak box is just a fiddle."

"Play it, Mr. Bob. Please play your fiddle," said Bonnie.

So Mr. Bob took his fiddle out of the squeak box and played a song they all knew. And his fiddle went, "Squeak, squeak, squeak."

73

# The Cobbler

Crooked heels
　And scuffy toes
Are all the kinds
　Of shoes he knows.

He patches up
　The broken places,
Sews the seams
　And shines their faces.

*Eleanor A. Chaffee*

74

## Father's Surprise

Bonnie and Billy left Mr. Bob's shop and started down the street.

"It's not time for Father to pick us up," said Bonnie. "Let's look in the store windows until he comes."

The children liked the little stores at Rainbow Corners. They were painted all colors of the rainbow.

There were flowers in front of some of the stores. The flowers were all colors of the rainbow too.

The children watched the cars and trucks go by as they waited.

"Let's play a guessing game while we wait," said Billy. "I guess the next car will be blue. Now, you guess!"

"I guess the next car will be a green car," said Bonnie.

Just then a long truck loaded with new cars went by.

"Look!" said Bonnie. "I see a green car on the truck."

"I can see a blue car on the truck, too," said Billy. "You guessed right and so did I."

76

Swish! Swish! went the cars as the children waited at the corner.

They saw the Rainbow Corners bus waiting at the bus stop. Bonnie and Billy waved to the bus driver.

A big milk truck came by on its way home from the city. The milk cans bumped up and down in the truck and made a loud noise.

Behind the milk truck came Mac's little car from the gasoline station.

"Why doesn't Father come?" said Billy. "He must have had trouble with the old truck again."

"Just wait!" said Bonnie. "Father will be here soon. The very next car may be his old green truck."

"Here comes something now," said Billy. "But it's not Father. It's a bus, a big school bus!"

"That's a big new school bus," said Bonnie. "Our old school bus is blue."

Honk! Honk! went the new school bus. Then it stopped at the corner.

Honk! Honk! the bus went again. The children looked at the driver.

"Bonnie!" called Billy. "It's Father! Father is in the new school bus."

78

"Jump in!" called Father. "Have
a ride in the new school bus! I'm the
new bus driver. Let's go home now and
surprise your mother."

Bonnie and Billy jumped into the new
school bus and away they went.

Soon they stopped at the door of the
farmhouse.

Honk! Honk! went the school bus.
The children were doing the honking
now. They were calling their mother.

Bonnie and Billy wanted Mother to see
the new school bus. They wanted her to
see the new bus driver too.

## Jingle, the Monkey

Bonnie and Billy had a wonderful day at the fair. Now it was time to go home. They were on their way to the truck with Father when they came to the merry-go-round.

"Oh, Father," said Bonnie. "Please may we ride on the big merry-go-round before we go?"

"Yes!" said Billy. "I would like to ride a bucking bronco, please, Father."

"Come and ride," called the man who was selling tickets. "Come and see Jingle the monkey dance."

The man had a long rope on Jingle. The little monkey danced and danced as the merry-go-round went around and around and around.

Bonnie and Billy had a good time on the merry-go-round. They had fun watching Jingle dance too.

"It's time to go," called Father. "We must go to the truck now. I have work to do at home."

81

"Look," said Bonnie. "See the man with all the bananas! May we buy some to take home? Mother likes bananas."

"Yes," said Father. "We will take some bananas home to Mother."

Father picked out some big yellow bananas. He put the bag of bananas in the back of the truck. Then they were ready to go home.

Father started the old truck. Out of the big gate they went and up the road toward home.

The truck stopped at the farmhouse and the children jumped out.

Mother called to them from the door. " Come and help me," she called. " Your pet lamb is out of his yard and he will not let me catch him ! "

The children ran to help Mother.

Father parked the old truck under a tree and jumped out. He was in a hurry to milk the cows.

Soon the lamb was back in his yard and Father was all through milking. The children sat on the back steps with Father and waited for their supper.

" Do you think we shall have bananas for supper ? " asked Bonnie.

" Did you bring the bananas in from the truck ? " asked Father.

" No, but I will get them right now," said Billy.

Billy ran out under the tree and looked in the back of the truck.

"Father, Father!" he called. "What has happened to the bananas? There are just two left in the bag. All the others are gone."

"Gone!" said Father. And he went to help Billy look for the bananas.

Just as Father got to the truck, something fell on Billy's head.

"It came down from the tree," said Father. "I saw it fall. I think it's a banana peeling!"

84

Bonnie and Mother came out to see what was happening. They looked up in the tree too.

"I saw something wiggle up in the leaves," called Bonnie.

"Where?" asked Billy.

"Right up there," said Bonnie. "It just wiggled again. See!"

"Whoever is up there had better come down!" called Billy.

They went on looking and looking. Soon they saw a brown tail moving in the leaves. Then a little face came peeping out.

"It's Jingle, the little monkey from the merry-go-round," shouted Billy. "He ate our bananas!"

Father laughed. "All monkeys like bananas," he said. "I guess this little monkey saw me put the bananas in the back of our truck."

"He must have climbed right into the truck after them!" said Bonnie.

"Now our bananas are gone," said Billy. "We have nothing left but the peelings!"

"What's more, we have a monkey named Jingle who does not belong to us," said Mother. "What are we going to do with him?"

Just then Jingle climbed down out of the tree and into the back of the truck. He gave a loud squeak and started to eat another banana!

"I have him now," called Father as he picked up the little monkey.

Father helped the children make a cage out of a big box. Then they put the little monkey in it.

The very next day the man from the merry-go-round came for Jingle. The man gave the children some tickets.

Then he said, "Come and ride on the merry-go-round again tomorrow. And this time I shall see that Jingle does not come home with you!"

# The Man from Mars

Mother called to the children from the top of the stairs.

"What time is it?" she asked.

"It's just about time for the Mars Space Show," called Billy.

"You may watch your TV show now," Mother said. "Then come upstairs to bed, please."

"Yes, we will, Mother," called the children. And they went on working on their pictures of the space show while they waited for it to start.

88

Billy showed his picture to Bonnie. "Doesn't this look like Mr. Mars' space ship?" he asked. "Let's turn on the TV, Bonnie. It's time for our space show."

Click, went the TV. Then the children began to watch their show. They wanted to find out if Mr. Mars would win the race in his space ship.

Zr! Zr! Zr—r—r! went all the space ships on the TV. Zr—r—r—r!

Just then the two children heard another noise. It was a loud bang.

The loud bang did not come from the TV. It came from right outside their own house.

"What's that?" cried Bonnie. She ran to the window and looked out.

"It's a thunder storm, Billy," called Bonnie. "Come and look at the trees blowing and swishing around!"

Billy did not move from his place in front of the TV. He wanted to see if Mr. Mars would win the race. One strange-looking ship had started to come nearer and nearer to Mr. Mars' big new space ship.

Just then the two children heard a noise. It was a very loud noise. Bang, bump, bump! it went.

Billy jumped up. "What was that?" he called. And he ran over to the big window and looked out.

"Something must have landed on our roof!" said Bonnie.

"The TV is off," said Billy. "And the lights have gone out!"

"Wait right where you are now, children," called Mother. "I will come down with the flashlight."

The children jumped back from the big window as the lightning flashed and the thunder roared.

"Look!" whispered Billy. "What is that outside our window, Bonnie? You can see it in the next lightning flash."

Bonnie peeped out of the window as the lightning flashed again. "I don't know," she whispered. "I wish Mother would come with the flashlight."

91

Just then the lightning flashed and the thunder roared again. So the children got another look at the strange-looking thing that was moving right outside the big window.

"Can it be a space ship, Billy?" asked Bonnie. "Or a rocket? Maybe the wind blew it down here."

Then the thunder roared over the house once again. The next flash of lightning was very bright.

"It moved!" said Billy. "I saw it right by the window. What is it?"

"Here I am, children," said Mother.
"I have found the flashlight at last.
Just listen to that thunder!"

"Mother," called Bonnie. "There is
something very strange right outside the
window. Please come over here with us
and look!"

"Hurry, Mother, hurry!" said Billy.
"It moved! And it thumped on the
window. Come and see what it is."

Mother went over to the big window
with the children. When she turned the
flashlight on the strange-looking thing,
she began to laugh.

93

"I see what it is," said Mother. "It is a strange-looking thing. It is our TV aerial. I guess the wind blew the aerial off the roof."

Bonnie looked at Billy, and Billy looked at Bonnie. Then they looked at the TV aerial and began to laugh.

"We thought the aerial was a man from Mars," said Billy.

"Or a space ship!" said Bonnie.

And they looked once more at the TV aerial moving in the wind just outside the window.

# Horses
## and
## Horses

## Fleetfoot's First Shoes

Once there was a pretty little colt named Fleetfoot. He did not like being a colt. He wanted to grow up and be a horse.

Every day Fleetfoot walked around the barnyard asking, "How soon will I grow up?"

One day Fleetfoot saw the big farm dog sleeping in the sun. So he asked, "How soon will I grow up?"

"All too soon," the old farm dog said. Then he went back to sleep.

" My mother will tell me," said the
little colt. So Fleetfoot went to her and
asked, " When will I grow up ? "

" Just as soon as you get your first
shoes," said his mother.

" Oh, Mother, may I have my first
shoes now ? " said Fleetfoot. " I want
to grow up and have a harness. Then
I can pull a shiny new carriage with
bright red wheels."

" You must grow, and wait," said
Fleetfoot's mother. "All colts have to
grow and wait for their first shoes."

One day Fleetfoot saw the farmer ride
out of the yard. He was in the shiny
new wagon, and Fleetfoot's mother was
pulling it.

Fleetfoot trotted out of the open gate
after the wagon. So the farmer let him
go along to the store.

Fleetfoot trotted along the road beside his mother. Now and then she called out to him.

"Watch out now, Fleetfoot!" said his mother. "Keep away from that fence! Look out for that big dog!"

When Fleetfoot almost ran into a hole by the side of the road, his mother called to him again.

"Watch out where you are going, Fleetfoot," she said. "You are not a little colt now. You are growing up, so you must watch out!"

Fleetfoot watched where he was going after this. He listened too. He listened to the click-clack of his mother's feet on the road. He liked the way her feet went

Click-clack,
Click-clack.

Soon the wagon stopped in front of the store. Fleetfoot trotted up to his mother and said, "I have just found out something. Your feet sing a song on the road. They say

99

Click-clack,
Click-clack."

Fleetfoot's mother said, "That is the horses' song. All horses' feet sing that song on the road."

"Will my feet sing it someday?" asked Fleetfoot.

"Yes, as soon as you get your first shoes," said his mother.

Days and days went by. Fleetfoot was growing up. Now he was almost as tall as his mother.

One day the farmer put a new harness on Fleetfoot and walked him all around in the yard.

100

"You are growing up, Fleetfoot," said the farmer. And he gave the colt a pat as he put him back into the barn with his mother.

One day Fleetfoot said, "Mother, how long will it be now before I get my shoes?"

"Any time now," said his mother. "We must wait and see."

Then bright and early one morning the farmer rode out of the farmyard gate on Fleetfoot's mother.

"Come with us, Fleetfoot," called the farmer. "We want you to go too."

Down the long road they went. Up one hill and down another! Then at last they stopped.

"Here we are, Fleetfoot," said his mother. "Are you ready for your first shoes? The man in the shop will put them on for you. Go with him now!"

Fleetfoot wanted his first shoes, so he went into the shop with the man. But Fleetfoot did not like the bright fire. He did not like the noise of the hammer.

102

Fleetfoot wanted to go back home. He called to his mother, "He-e-e-e!"

"It's all right, Fleetfoot," she said. "It's all right. Just hold still. This will be over soon."

So the big man with the hammer put some shoes on Fleetfoot. As the man worked, his big hammer said,

"New shoes, new shoes,
New shoes for Fleetfoot!"

Now Fleetfoot had his first shoes and he was ready to go home!

103

The farmer rode on Fleetfoot's mother and Fleetfoot trotted along by her side. Soon they were on the long road to the farm. Fleetfoot listened.

Yes, his new shoes were singing the horses' song,

> " Click-clack,
> Click-clack,
> There and back.
> Click-clack,
> Click-clack."

Now at last Fleetfoot was happy.

104

# A New Little Colt

A new little colt is awfully sweet,
He has four long legs and four short feet
And a small round body with soft, soft hair
And big brown eyes and ears up in the air
And a nose like smooth velvet and a soft little neigh
As he kicks up his heels and prances away.

*Zhenya Gay*

105

# The Taxicab Horse

Taffy, the old gray taxicab horse, was standing by the gate at the animal fair. He had been there a long time and he was hungry.

All at once the gate opened and out came two rabbits. The two rabbits had a big basket of carrots with them.

" Such carrots ! " said Merry.

" The best I ever saw ! " said Cherry. " But how shall we ever get them home ? "

"What you rabbits need is a taxicab," called Taffy.

Merry and Cherry stopped and put down the big basket of carrots.

"I am a taxicab horse," said Taffy. "Get on and I will take you home."

"We have no money to pay for a taxicab horse," said Merry.

"We bought so many carrots that our money is all gone," said Cherry.

Taffy looked at the carrots and said, "You don't need money. Just tie your basket up here by my head and hop on my back."

107

Merry and Cherry got on Taffy's back and away they all went.

The rabbits had a wonderful time. They had never been on a taxicab horse before. They laughed and sang. They called to friends along the way.

Taffy went on down the long road. He didn't say a word. But Taffy was hungry, so he ate one little carrot. Then he ate another.

The carrots were so good that Taffy went right on eating them.

Soon they came to the big woods.

" Stop, please," called Merry and Cherry.
" We want to get off here. Thank you
for the ride."

" Thank you," called Taffy. " That was
a good supper." Then off down the road
he went.

Merry looked at Cherry and Cherry
looked at Merry. Then they looked at
the basket of carrots.

The rabbits counted the carrots once.
They counted them again. And each time
they came out with four. There were just
four big carrots left in the basket.

"Oh, well!" said Cherry. "Four big carrots are better than no carrots."

"That's right!" said Merry. "And the ride was fun. A basket of carrots is not much to pay for a taxicab ride."

Merry took two carrots, and Cherry took two carrots. Then they went home. They wanted to tell their friends how much fun it was to go to the animal fair.

But the two rabbits thought the ride home on the taxicab horse had been the most fun of all.

110

# Bonnie Bess

This is the story of a beautiful black trotting horse named Bonnie Bess.

She did not live in the barn with the other horses. She did not pull a wagon for the farmer. She did not eat the green grass that grew on the hillside nearby.

Bonnie Bess was a weathervane horse. She lived at the top of the farmer's barn. She turned around and around and around to show the way the wind was blowing.

Bonnie Bess had been on top of the farmer's barn for a long, long time.

111

Bonnie Bess was happy, as the wind blew her around and around. When the wind blew from the east, she turned and trotted toward the east.

Then the farmer said, " Bess says it's going to rain." So he brought his hay in from the field.

When the wind blew from the west, Bess trotted toward the west.

Then the farmer said, " Bess says we will have a good day." So he went out to plant his corn.

" My Bess is a wonderful weathervane horse," said the farmer each day when his work was over.

Then he sat down under a big tree and looked at his fields and his barn. He looked at Bonnie Bess, too, as she turned and turned high up on the roof of his big red barn.

112

One day the farmer moved away. He took his hens and his ducks. He took his cows and his horses and his lambs.

He loaded all his chairs and tables and beds and dishes on a big, big wagon and rode away.

He took his mailbox with him, too, but he did not take Bonnie Bess.

He left her turning in the wind on top of the big barn. Around and around and around she went.

Now the house was empty and so was the barn. Nothing but Bonnie Bess was left behind.

Years and years went by. The barn
grew old. The roof fell in and the paint
peeled off the sides.

Still Bonnie Bess went on turning.
Around and around in the wind she
went. From east to west and from west
to east, Bonnie Bess turned as the winds
blew.

One day in winter a cold wind blew
and blew. It blew Bonnie Bess right off
the barn and over to the side of the
road. She landed in a big pile of snow.

114

A man in a truck came down the road.
He saw Bonnie Bess, so he stopped and
picked her up.

"A very fine weathervane horse!" he
said. "It is many years old. I'll take it
along to my shop."

Then the man bumped along the road
until he came to his little shop.

Outside the shop were some old wagon
wheels and some old chairs.

The sign over the shop said,

The Old, Old Shop
We Sell Everything

There were all kinds of things in the little shop, and most of them were many years old.

There were so many things in the shop that there was not much room for Bonnie Bess. But the man found a place for her near an old bicycle, and there she stayed for a long time.

Each day people came into the shop to look around. They bought old cups, old chairs, and old wagon wheels, but no one wanted an old weathervane horse.

116

One day a farmer came into the shop
to look around. He looked at everything
in the shop.

When the farmer saw Bonnie Bess he
said, " I have bought a farm not far from
here. I have a big red barn. This is
just the weathervane I want to put on
the top of my barn."

So the farmer bought Bonnie Bess and
took her away in his truck. Over the
country roads they bumped. Then at last
the truck stopped.

117

The truck stopped right in front of the barn where Bonnie Bess had lived for so many years. But now the old barn looked like new.

The farmer climbed up on a long, long ladder and put Bonnie Bess back on top of the barn. She started to work right away. Around and around and around she turned.

Sometimes she turned to the east.

Sometimes she turned to the west.

Bonnie Bess was happy to be on the old barn once more. She was happy to be at work again.

The farmer thought Bonnie Bess was the best weathervane horse in the country. And she was!

## The Talking Horse

Hayboy was a big brown horse who lived in Mr. Row's barn. Hayboy looked like many other horses, but some people thought he was different. They said he could talk.

Little Patsy Purple said so. Patsy lived right next door to Mr. Row. She came to see Hayboy every day.

One morning Patsy thought she heard someone in the barn say, "I could help Mr. Row if he-e-e would ask me-e-e!"

There was no one in the barn but Hayboy and Patsy.

Patsy knew why Hayboy was talking. He wanted to help Mr. Row. Mr. Row had rabbit trouble. Some nights he could not sleep because of the rabbits.

There were big rabbits and there were little rabbits, and they all made trouble for Mr. Row. They were in his garden every night, all night long!

One night Mr. Row jumped out of bed and ran out to his garden. He shouted at the rabbits. He splashed them with water from the sprinkler, but it didn't do any good.

120

The next morning Mr. Row went to look at his garden. Hayboy went along and so did Patsy Purple.

Row after row of the little cabbage plants were gone.

"Rabbit trouble! Rabbit trouble!" shouted Mr. Row. "What can I do?"

"Let's ask Hayboy," said Patsy Purple. "He might tell us. He is a talking horse, you know."

Mr. Row laughed. "Whoever heard of a talking horse!" he said. "I'll go and ask my friends in town what to do."

Then Mr. Row harnessed Hayboy to the wagon and went straight to town.

He found his friend the policeman and asked him if he knew what to do for rabbit trouble.

"I don't know what to do," said the policeman. "Ask the grocer."

So Mr. Row asked the grocer. Then he asked the butcher, the bus driver, and the baker. But they didn't know what to do for rabbit trouble.

Mr. Row couldn't think of anyone else to ask. So he got into his wagon and Hayboy headed for home.

Hayboy knew where he was going, and he knew just what he was going to do when he got there.

Patsy Purple was on the garden fence waiting when Hayboy and Mr. Row came back from town.

"Look at the rabbits!" said Patsy. "You still have rabbit trouble."

"Trouble! Trouble!" said Mr. Row. He got out of the wagon and began to take off Hayboy's harness. "What shall I do?"

Patsy jumped off the fence and ran over to Hayboy.

"Hayboy, please tell Mr. Row what to do for rabbit trouble," said Patsy.

Then Hayboy started talking—but he started talking to the rabbits.

"Listen, all you rabbits," said Hayboy. "I am going to tell you something right now. Listen to me-e-e!"

123

The rabbits stopped eating and listened with their long ears.

"You rabbits know you must not eat Mr. Row's cabbage," said Hayboy. "You know there is good food for you in the woods and fields. Go and find it, all of you! Go! Get out of this garden!"

Then all the rabbits began to hop. Out of the garden and up the long hill they all went.

"I told you Hayboy was a talking horse," said Patsy Purple. "I knew it all the time."

Mr. Row gave Hayboy a pat on the back. Mr. Row was so happy he couldn't say a word. At last his rabbit trouble was all over!

124

ALONG
CITY STREETS

## Excitement on Applegate Street

Joe had a tooth that wiggled. It was a big front tooth. It wiggled when he talked, and it wiggled when he ate.

Joe was thinking about his tooth as he walked down Applegate Street. He was thinking about the wish he would make when his tooth came out.

There was something that Joe wanted very much. He was going to wish for it and see what happened.

126

Just then Joe saw a manhole that had been opened in the street.

Around the manhole was a little red fence. And on the fence was a big sign that said,

Men Working

Joe stopped. He could hear the men working, but he could not see them. They were doing something far down inside the hole.

Joe wanted to see what was going on. So he went a little nearer.

Just then Joe sneezed. It was a big sneeze, and out of Joe's mouth jumped his big front tooth.

127

Joe's tooth bounced right across the sidewalk. Down, down into the open manhole it rolled.

"My tooth! I sneezed and lost my tooth!" Joe cried. "I want my tooth."

All at once the men down in the manhole stopped hammering. They all started shouting.

"I'll get it," called one of the men.

He climbed up the ladder and came out of the manhole. Then he started running down the street.

128

"It was just a tooth," Joe called. But the man did not hear him. He went right on running.

Then a big truck came up the street. Some men with picks and shovels jumped out of the truck.

Joe thought it was fun to see all the excitement on Applegate Street!

Soon the people came out of the stores to see what was the matter, and they stayed to watch all the excitement. A policeman came and made the people keep out of the street.

"It was just a tooth," Joe called to the policeman. "It fell out when I sneezed, but I want to put it under my pillow."

The policeman was much too busy to listen to Joe.

"Move back now," said the policeman. "Move back from the street. Stay on the sidewalk, please."

Then the machines came. They went to work on the street. Clinkety-clank! Bump, bump, bump, they went!

Never before had Joe seen so many machines and so much excitement!

130

All at once there was a big, big
whoo-sh! Then out of another hole in
the street came water. It went almost
as high as the buildings.

The water splashed all over the people.
They ran to get out of the way. There
had never been so much excitement on
Applegate Street before.

Someone shouted, "It's a big water
pipe! Hurry! Turn off the water!"

The workmen climbed in and out of
the manhole. And at last the water
stopped coming up out of the hole in
the street.

All at once Joe heard someone calling his name. It was his father. He had stopped with the other people to watch all the excitement.

"Come on, Joe," said Father. "Let's go home now."

"Did they find my tooth, Father?" asked Joe.

"Your tooth!" said Father.

"Yes," said Joe. "I sneezed and my tooth fell into the manhole. I guess all the men have been looking for it."

132

"No, Joe," said his father. "There was a break in a water pipe under Applegate Street. That's what all the excitement is about. I don't think you will get your tooth back."

"But I want it," said Joe. "I want to put it under my pillow. I want to wish on it. Now I cannot wish for a little black dog."

Father looked at Joe and laughed.

Then he said, "Do you know, Joe, a tooth under a street may work better than a tooth under a pillow!"

133

That night when Joe went to sleep, his tooth was not under his pillow. It was under the street, but Joe made a wish just the same.

When morning came, there was a little black dog beside Joe's bed.

After that, when Joe walked down Applegate Street, the little black dog went along with him.

And this all happened because of Joe's tooth and the excitement that day on Applegate Street.

134

# Ellie, the Elephant

Ellie was a great big elephant. She lived in the park in a big city.

All the children who came to the park liked Ellie. But the one who liked Ellie best was Teeny. She was a little girl who lived near the park. Every day Teeny came to see Ellie.

Before long the great big elephant and the little girl became the very best of friends.

Teeny would wave her hand and call, "Ellie, how are you today? Did you have a good breakfast this morning?"

Then Ellie would wave back to Teeny with her long trunk.

One day while Teeny was in the park, some men came in a big truck. They came with their truck to take Ellie away to another city.

Teeny cried and cried because her big friend Ellie was going away.

Now the great big elephant and the very little girl would never see each other again.

Teeny waved good-by to Ellie. And Ellie waved back with her long trunk as the truck rolled away.

Ellie did not want to leave the park. She did not want to leave her little friend Teeny.

136

The truck went on and on. But Ellie would not look at the big trees or the houses or the people. She looked straight ahead, for she was very sad.

After a long time the truck began to slow down. It was slowing down because it was coming to an underpass.

An underpass is a place where the road runs under a bridge. Trains or cars run on the bridge that is over the road.

This was not a very big underpass. It was not high enough for a truck with a big elephant on it to get through.

The men stopped the truck near the underpass. They didn't know what to do.

They looked up at Ellie. Then they looked at the underpass.

"We shall never make it," said one man. "We shall never get her through."

Then the men tried to get Ellie off the truck. They shouted at her, but she would not get off the truck.

Ellie just waved her trunk and looked very, very tall.

"What an elephant!" said the men. "What shall we do with her?"

138

Soon there was a long line of cars behind the truck. They wanted to get through the underpass too.

Some of the drivers honked their horns. Some laughed at the elephant who could not go under the bridge. But they were all in a hurry. They wanted to move on.

Some of the men in the cars got out to help, but no one could think of a way to get Ellie through the underpass. She just stayed on the truck and looked very, very tall.

There was nothing the men in the truck could do but turn around and take Ellie back to the park.

When the truck came to the elephant house, there was Teeny! She was busy feeding the sparrows and pigeons nearby.

Teeny didn't know where Ellie had been. She didn't know why Ellie had come back. But she was, oh, so glad to see her!

As for Ellie, she thought the park was the most beautiful place in all the world. And maybe she was right!

140

## Chipper, the Sparrow

The bright morning sun peeped out from behind the trees in the city park. Across the street little Chipper Sparrow looked out from under the roof of the old Graystone Hotel.

"Coo-e-e! Chipper! Hurry! Get up!" It was Pigeon calling. He was Chipper Sparrow's best friend.

"I saw a new popcorn machine in the park," said Pigeon.

"Popcorn!" said Chipper. "Oh, bird!" And he flew down to the hotel sign beside his friend Pigeon.

141

"Let's go and find some popcorn now before all the starlings get there," said Pigeon. The two birds left the Graystone Hotel and flew to the city park across the street.

"I can see the popcorn machine," said Pigeon. "And a Person has just bought some popcorn. Look! Some of it fell on the ground."

"Oh, bird!" said Chipper. "How I like a Person who drops things."

The two birds flew down to the walk near the popcorn machine. But before Chipper and Pigeon could get any of the popcorn, along came the starlings.

"We saw the popcorn first," shouted Chipper. "That is our popcorn!"

"Who said so?" called a starling as he started toward Chipper.

"Come on, Chipper," called Pigeon. "I see Boxer the dog on the walk. He is with the Person who belongs to him. Let's talk to Boxer." Away they flew.

"How are you, Boxer?" said Chipper. "Are you busy this morning?"

"Not too busy!" said Boxer. "My Person is reading a magazine just now."

"I wish I had a Person to take care of," said Chipper. "A small Person!"

143

Pigeon turned around and looked back at the starlings.

"Look, Boxer!" said Pigeon. "The starlings took our place at the popcorn machine. Will you help us?"

"Wrrrf!" barked Boxer. "Just watch me! Wrrrf!" And Boxer made all the starlings fly out of the park.

"Thank you, Boxer," said Pigeon and Chipper. "Now we can eat the popcorn."

"Good-by!" said Boxer. "It's time for me to go home with my Person. He has stopped reading his magazine now."

Chipper looked up as they ate the last of the popcorn.

"Look, Pigeon! Here comes another Person," said Chipper. "It's a small one. She has her doll out for an airing."

"Oh, that's not a doll," said Pigeon. "That's a yellow cat."

"It must be a doll," said Chipper. "It's in a doll carriage."

Chipper flew over and looked in the doll carriage. There on a pink pillow sat a big yellow cat.

"Oh, bird!" said Chipper. "What kind of doll is this?"

145

"Stop looking at me!" said the cat on the pillow. "I'm just doing this to make my small Person happy."

"I wish I had a small Person," said Chipper. "Someday I will have one."

"How will you find one, Chipper?" asked Pigeon.

"Boxer found a big Person," said Chipper. "Yellow Cat found a little Person. I guess I can find one too. I will just follow this street out to the country." And away Chipper flew.

Over the rows of houses toward the country Chipper went. At last he saw green fields and big red barns.

146

In a yard near a big barn Chipper saw many hens. So he flew down into the yard with them.

A big hen saw Chipper and called, "Go away! We are prize hens. We do not want a sparrow in our yard."

Chipper flew on until he came to a picnic place near a river.

Some people were eating their picnic lunch not far from the little bridge. So Chipper flew down near the bridge and began to look for something to eat.

Just then Chipper heard a small boy talking. "Come here, little sparrow," said the boy. "Come here and get this apple peeling."

Chipper looked at the apple peeling on the grass. "Chip! Chip!" he said.

"Come on," said the boy. "Come on. Chip! Chip! Chipper!"

"He knows my name," said Chipper. "He may be the small Person for me."

Chipper was eating the peeling as the boy's father called, "Bob, it's time to go now."

" This little sparrow is talking to me, Father," said Bob.

Father said, " It does sound like it. But we must go home now. Come along and get into the car, Bob."

In a flash, Chipper was in the car too. He landed right on top of the picnic basket near Bob.

" Going home with us, Chipper ? " asked Father as he started the car.

Off down the long road they went. Then at last, Father stopped the car.

Chipper flew out of the open door. He looked all around. He saw a tall apartment house near a park. Across the street was the Graystone Hotel.

" Chip ! Chip ! " said Chipper. " I am home." And he tried to tell Bob that he would see him soon over in the park. Tomorrow, maybe !

149

The next morning Chipper and Pigeon left the hotel early. They flew to the park to look for Bob. They saw him talking to the man by the new popcorn machine.

Chipper and Pigeon flew down to the walk nearby.

"Chip! Chip! Chip!" said Chipper.

"It's Chipper!" said Bob. "It's the sparrow that was at the picnic! He knows me! I will get him some popcorn."

Now Chipper was a very happy little sparrow. He had a small Person all his own at last.

# Mrs. Peck-Pigeon

Mrs. Peck-Pigeon
Is picking for bread,
Bob-bob-bob
Goes her little round head.
Tame as a pussy-cat
In the street,
Step-step-step
Go her little red feet.
With her little red feet
And her little round head,
Mrs. Peck-Pigeon
Goes picking for bread.

*Eleanor Farjeon*

# Beedle and Mr. Bean

Mr. Bean and his horse Beedle lived together in the city. Beedle was old now, but he was still very smart.

Beedle had once been a show horse. When people talked to him, he would paw the ground and bow his head.

Mr. Bean had been a showman at one time, but now he was old too. He liked to talk things over with Beedle.

"Shall we take the money out of my old trunk and buy a small magazine stand, Beedle?" asked Mr. Bean.

Up and down went Beedle's head.

Mr. Bean bought a small magazine stand on a busy corner, and he and Beedle were very happy about it.

They opened the stand very early the first morning. In a short time, people had bought seven newspapers and five TV magazines.

All at once Mr. Bean called out to Beedle. " I did not bring the candy. How can we run our magazine stand without candy ? "

Beedle pawed the ground very fast as Mr. Bean watched him.

" That's right, Beedle," said Mr. Bean. " You can take care of the stand while I go home and get some boxes of candy. You are a smart horse."

Up and down went Beedle's head.

Mr. Bean took off Beedle's harness, and put him in the magazine stand.

Mr. Bean laughed when he saw Beedle inside the stand.

"Beedle, I think you look like me," he said.

He took off his hat and put it on Beedle's head. He took off his coat and put it around Beedle. Then Mr. Bean started for home in a hurry.

Beedle looked at all the bright new magazines. Then he bowed to Mr. King who came up to the stand.

"I want a newspaper," said Mr. King as he put down his money. "And the magazine 'How to Make Money.'"

Beedle nosed a magazine toward Mr. King. It was called " Fishing."

Mr. King did not stop to look at the magazine. He was in a big hurry!

Beedle nosed the money along until it fell into the money box. Beedle was a smart horse!

Other people came by in a hurry. They picked up their newspapers and magazines without looking at Beedle.

Then Mrs. Peters said, " I want the magazine called 'Today's Dishes.'"

Beedle nosed a big magazine toward Mrs. Peters. It was " Today's Dances."

Mr. Bean came hurrying back to the stand with the candy. He was much surprised to see all the money Beedle had in the money box. Now they could put some money back into the trunk.

"Beedle, you have been working like a horse!" said Mr. Bean. He opened the candy and gave some to Beedle.

"Let me have my hat and coat now and I will take over your job," said Mr. Bean.

Beedle ate the candy as he waited for Mr. Bean. What good candy it was!

Soon Mrs. Peters came by the stand in a pretty new dress.

"Oh, Mr. Bean," she called. "I like this magazine. I was going to spend the day in the kitchen. Now I think I shall go and learn to dance."

"Thank you for selling me the new magazine 'Fishing,'" called Mr. King. "Fishing is just what I want to do."

Mr. Bean looked at Beedle and Beedle looked at Mr. Bean. Then they laughed and laughed.

"Beedle," said Mr. Bean. "You are a smart horse, a very smart horse."

157

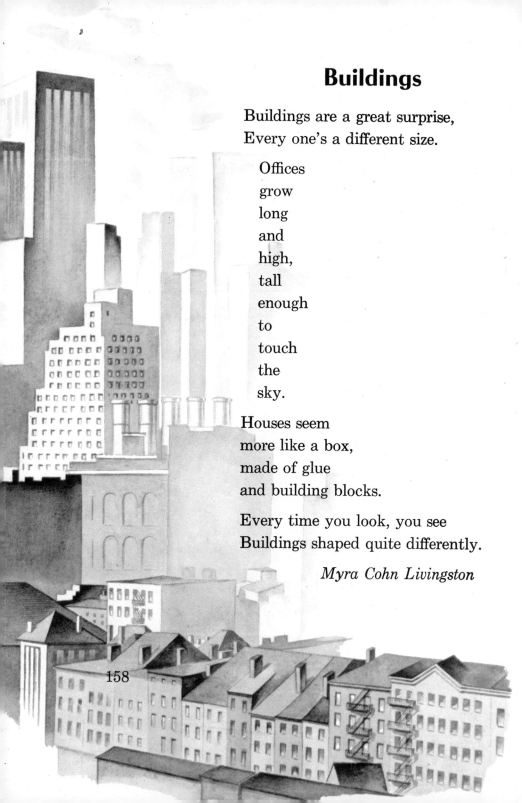

# Buildings

Buildings are a great surprise,
Every one's a different size.

Offices
grow
long
and
high,
tall
enough
to
touch
the
sky.

Houses seem
more like a box,
made of glue
and building blocks.

Every time you look, you see
Buildings shaped quite differently.

*Myra Cohn Livingston*

158

159

Old, Old Stories

## Hans Has Three Meals

One morning very early Hans started out to look for work. He had to walk a long way to reach the town. When he got there, he was very hungry.

Hans walked up to a farmer who was standing by the open door of his house. "My name is Hans," he said. "Have you work that I can do?"

"Is your work good, Hans?" asked the farmer.

"That I will leave for you to find out," said Hans.

Hans could see a good hot breakfast on the table in the house. He looked at the food with longing.

"Do I get something to eat if I work for you?" asked Hans.

The farmer laughed. "Yes, Hans," he said. "You do."

"How many meals?" asked Hans.

"Three meals—breakfast, dinner, and supper!" said the farmer.

Then Hans asked, "Will you give me breakfast now?"

"Yes, sit down here," said the farmer. "Eat all you want."

The farmer's wife brought a bowl of hot food and Hans ate it all.

"Now we must go to work, Hans," said the farmer.

Hans got up and started toward the door, but he stopped by the stove.

"Will you let me ask you one little thing more?" said Hans.

"Ask anything that you please, Hans," said the farmer.

"I was just thinking," said Hans. "Why not have dinner now?"

"Dinner!" said the farmer. "Why, it's still early in the morning."

The farmer's wife heard what Hans said. She went over to the farmer and whispered, "If he eats now, he will not have to come back to the house for his next meal. That will give him more time to work."

162

The farmer's wife put a big dish of cabbage soup on the stove. She put milk and butter in the soup. Then Hans' next meal was ready.

Hans started eating at once and before long his dish was empty. He got up from the table and with slow steps started for the door. Then he turned and looked back into the kitchen.

"Did I hear you say something about supper?" asked Hans.

"We have supper here every night," said the farmer.

Once again the farmer's wife pulled the farmer to one side.

"Let him have his supper now," she whispered. "It is a long way from the field to the house. If he eats now, he will not have to walk all the way back for his supper."

"You are right," said the farmer. "Then he will have more time to work."

So the farmer's wife cut some bread and put some butter on it. She cut some yellow cheese and some white cheese. Then she put the cheese and bread on the table.

Hans sat down at the table to eat. How good the cheese was! Soon the bread and cheese were almost gone.

The farmer watched Hans from the doorway. At last he asked, "Are you ready to work now, Hans?"

Hans ate the last of the good cheese and got up from the table.

"I'm coming," said Hans.

The farmer said, "We must get an ax to carry with us. Then we shall be ready for a good day's work."

"Work!" said Hans in surprise. "Do you want me to work now?"

"Yes," said the farmer. "It is still early in the day."

"But I have just had my supper," said Hans. "At home we always go to sleep after supper."

Hans saw a big pile of hay in the barn. He threw himself down on it, and almost at once he went to sleep.

The farmer called to Hans, but it was no use. Hans went right on sleeping as he always did at home after supper.

166

# The Merchant and His Servants

Once upon a time there was an old merchant who had many servants. The old merchant wanted to go to another city to sell his goods.

So he got together all the things he wished to sell. There were treasures of silver and treasures of gold and beautiful silks of many colors.

The old merchant and his servants would be gone two days and a night. So they had to carry a great basket of bread for the trip.

The merchant called all his servants together when everything was ready.

"Here are the things I wish to take with me," he said. "Each of you will carry one burden. You may carry any burden you wish."

The servants looked over the big piles of goods. Then a small servant in a red coat picked up the largest burden of all. It was the great basket of bread.

The other servants laughed at him.

"That is the largest burden of all," they said. "Our burdens are not so large as yours."

The old merchant started out with all his servants. They went a long, long way under the hot sun.

The small servant could not go very fast with his great basket of bread. So he walked along behind the others.

When it was time to eat, the old merchant stopped by a spring.

"Give each man bread to eat," called the merchant to the servant who was carrying the basket of bread.

The servant did as he was told and soon all the men were eating.

When night came, the merchant and his servants stopped again. This time they were very hungry, so they ate almost all the bread in the basket.

The next morning the merchant and his servants ate the last of the bread. Again they started on their way to the city with their burdens.

The small servant picked up the great bread basket. But it was not the largest burden now, for the basket was empty.

The other servants were all carrying the same burdens.

The merchant saw this and said, " The small servant is a smart servant. He had the largest burden when we started. Now he has no burden at all."

170

# The Three Wishes

An old man and his wife lived in a little old house in the woods. One cold winter night they sat in front of a small fire and talked about their many troubles.

"This old house is cold," said the wife. "It is not good enough for a donkey to live in."

"What shall we do?" asked the man. "We are old and poor. There is no one to help us. We have no money and we have no children."

"We have nothing but dry bread for our supper," said the old woman.

Just then the wind blew some smoke down the chimney. At the same time, the wife saw a little fairy standing in front of the fire.

"You poor old people," said the little fairy. "I heard what you said and I would like to help you."

The old man and his wife were too surprised to move.

"I will give you three wishes," said the fairy. "The next three things you wish for will be yours." Then the fairy was gone.

"Did you hear that?" said the old woman. "We can wish for anything we want. Anything at all!"

"Yes, Wife, I heard," said the old man. "But I am hungry, so let's have our supper first."

While the two old people ate their supper of dry bread, they talked about the things they wanted.

The old woman wanted a big house. The old man wanted money, much money.

"We must have children too," said the old woman.

"Yes," said the old man. "We will wish for many children!"

The old man and his wife went on talking and eating.

"We will have good food," said the old woman. "I am hungry now. I wish I had a sausage for my supper this very night."

At once the two old people heard a bump, bump, in the chimney, and there on the table was a big sausage.

"Wife! Wife! See what you have done!" said the old man. "Now one of our three wishes is gone, and we have nothing but a sausage. I wish it were at the end of your nose!"

At once the sausage jumped up and was soon sticking to the end of the old woman's nose.

"Now see what you have done!" cried the old woman. "Come and help me get this sausage off my nose."

So the old man pulled and his wife pulled. Then the two of them pulled. But they could not get the sausage off the end of the old woman's nose.

"Stop!" cried the old woman. "My poor nose! We have just one more wish. We must wish this sausage off my nose."

175

"But what of the big new house?"
said the old man.

"No! No!" cried the wife. "I want
this sausage off my nose. Right now!"

"But what of the money?" said the
old man. "We wanted some money."

"It doesn't matter," said the wife.
"Money will do me no good if I have to
go around with a sausage at the end of
my nose. We must make our last wish."

Then the little fairy was standing before
the fire again.

"And what is your last wish?" she
asked the old people.

"We want to wish this sausage off the end of my wife's nose," the old man said to the fairy.

At once the big sausage was gone and so was the fairy.

The three wishes were gone too. So the old man and the old woman sat in front of their little fire again.

Everything was just as it had been before the fairy came. They had no big house, no money, and no children. They were just as they had been before the fairy gave them the three wishes.

177

## The Lost Donkey

There was once a farmer who made his living by growing wheat on his land. As soon as the wheat was ready, he took it to the mill. Then the wheat was ground into flour.

One day the farmer made ready for his trip to the mill. He tied the bags of wheat onto the backs of seven of his donkeys.

The farmer had eight donkeys, so there was one left for him to ride.

Just as the farmer was about to get
on the back of the last donkey, he called
to his wife.

"I am ready to go now," he said.
"I have our eight donkeys with me, and
I shall take care that not one of them
is lost."

Then the farmer climbed on the back
of the last donkey. He waved to his
wife, and started off on his trip to the
mill with his wheat.

179

The donkeys all followed one another along down the road. After a while the farmer counted the donkeys in the line ahead of him.

"Seven!" he cried. "I can count just seven donkeys. One of the donkeys is missing. I must go and look for the donkey that is lost."

So the farmer climbed down from his donkey. He ran here and he ran there looking for the lost animal. But the missing donkey could not be found.

"I will look once more behind that big rock over there," said the farmer.

The lost donkey was not behind the big rock. So the farmer came back to the road.

"I will count the donkeys once more before I go on," he said to himself. Then, "One, two, three, four . . ." On up to eight he counted.

"Eight donkeys!" said the farmer. "There are eight donkeys here now. So the lost donkey must have come back while I was away looking for him."

The farmer climbed on his donkey once again and started down the road on his way to the mill.

By and by the farmer stopped at a spring to give his donkeys some water. While they were drinking, he counted the donkeys once more. And again he counted just seven donkeys.

"That animal is lost again!" said the farmer. "How in the world did he get away from the others?"

Just then the farmer saw a traveler who was about to stop at the spring. The traveler had been watching the farmer as he counted the donkeys.

182

"Help me count my donkeys!" called the farmer. And he told the traveler all about his trouble with the lost donkey.

"One, two, three . . ." counted the traveler. And he counted up to eight. "You have eight donkeys now," said the traveler.

"Eight!" said the farmer. "But I counted seven. I know I left home with eight. I think someone must be playing a trick on me."

The traveler said, "Come and stand over here with me."

The farmer walked over to the place where the traveler was standing.

"I think I know what your trouble is," said the traveler. "You counted seven donkeys when you rode on your donkey behind the others. You did not count the donkey that you rode."

The farmer thanked the traveler for his help. Then each went his own way.

The farmer did not count his donkeys again. But when he got home to his good wife, the donkeys were all there. All eight of them!

# The Honest Woodcutter

Once a poor but honest woodcutter was at work beside a beautiful lake. He cut first on one side of a big tree and then he cut on the other.

"One more blow with my good ax and this big tree will fall," said the woodcutter to himself.

Just then his ax flew out of his hands and went down into the lake with a big splash. The woodcutter sat down on a log and put his head in his hands.

185

"What shall I do?" said the poor woodcutter. "If I have no ax, then I cannot cut down trees to earn money. If I have no money, I cannot buy food for my wife and children."

Just then a fairy dressed all in white came up out of the lake.

"Here is your ax," she called.

The woodcutter jumped up from the log and reached for the ax. Then he saw that the ax was made of gold.

"Thank you, kind fairy," said the honest woodcutter. "But that is not my ax. My ax was not made of gold."

186

Down into the lake went the beautiful water fairy. Soon she came up out of the water again.

"Is this your ax?" she called to the poor woodcutter.

The woodcutter looked down at the beautiful ax in the fairy's hand.

Then he said, "Thank you, kind fairy. But that ax does not belong to me. My ax was not made of silver."

Again the water fairy went down into the lake, and again she came up with an ax.

"Here is your ax," said the fairy. "You are an honest woodcutter. You would not take an ax that was not your own. Now you shall have all three."

"Oh, thank you! Thank you, kind fairy!" said the honest woodcutter.

The water fairy went down into the lake and did not come back again.

"How happy my good wife will be to hear about the kind fairy," said the woodcutter to himself. And he put the gold and silver axes with his coat under a tree near the lake.

Then the honest woodcutter took his good ax and went back to work. How he made the woods ring as he cut down tree after tree!

188

# An Old Rhyme

If all the seas were one sea,
What a *great* sea that would be!

If all the trees were one tree,
What a *great* tree that would be!

And if all the axes were one axe,
What a *great* axe that would be!

And if all the men were one man,
What a *great* man that would be!

And if the *great* man took the *great* axe,
And cut down the *great* tree,

And let it fall in the *great* sea,
What a splish-splash that would be!

*Traditional*

189

# To the Teacher

*Ranches and Rainbows* is the fourth book in a series of Enrichment Readers for the GINN BASIC READING SERIES. Written at second-reader level, *Ranches and Rainbows* follows the basic Second Reader, *Around the Corner*, and precedes the basic Third Reader, *Finding New Neighbors*. This Enrichment Reader introduces 86 new words, 33 of which are introduced in the revised basic Third Readers. It re-introduces and maintains 305 words from the Second Readers of the GINN BASIC READERS, Revised. The lines in the word list indicate the beginning of a new unit or story.

## New Words in This Book

UNIT I
7. . . .
———
8. Randy
   Rocket
9. . . .
10. . . .
11. swish
12. . . .
———
13. Jill
    corral
14. feed
    toward
15. . . .
16. . . .
———
17. rodeo
18. buck
    bronco
19. . . .
20. . . .
21. . . .
———
22. *Poem*
———
23. calves
24. . . .

25. . . .
26. . . .
27. . . .
28. . . .
29. . . .
30. . . .
———
UNIT II
31. . . .
———
32. . . .
33. . . .
34. . . .
35. shell
36. . . .
37. . . .
———
38. *Poem*
———
39. . . .
40. . . .
41. . . .
42. seats
43. whispered
44. . . .
45. trouble
46. early

47. . . .
48. . . .
49. . . .
50. . . .
51. belong
———
52. moving
53. Bridget
54. . . .
55. . . .
56. carriage
57. . . .
58. . . .
59. . . .
———
60. Fisherman
    butcher
61. grocer
62. line
63. . . .
64. . . .
65. . . .
66. . . .
———
UNIT III
67. Rainbow
———
68. squeak
    Bonnie's

69. . . .
70. . . .
71. . . .
72. . . .
73. fiddle
———
74. *Poem*
———
75. . . .
76. . . .
77. . . .
78. . . .
79. . . .
———
80. . . .
81. . . .
82. bananas
83. . . .
84. peeling
85. wiggle
86. . . .
87. . . .
———
88. Mars
    space
89. ship
90. thunder
91. lightning

190

92. . . .
93. . . .
94. aerial

Illustrations by: Peter Burchard, Bruno Frost, Ed Gordon, Paul Granger, Allen Johnson, Cynthia Koehler, Marie Nonnast, Tommy Shoemaker, and George Withers.

PRINTED IN THE UNITED STATES OF AMERICA